# Antiquity Unveiled

## Masterworks, 1760–1840

## Koopman Rare Art

An exhibition of neo-classical silver for sale

at Koopman Rare Art
53–64 Chancery Lane WC2A 1QS
tel. 020 7242 7624/fax 020 7831 0221
www.koopmanrareart.com

3–25 June 2010

This exhibition of selections from our stock is being held concurrently with the loan exhibition

# The Classical Ideal

**English Silver, 1760–1840**

3–25 June 2010

Edited and produced by John Adamson



A catalogue record for this book is available from the British Library.

Published by John Adamson
90 Hertford Street, Cambridge CB4 3AQ, England
for Koopman Rare Art Ltd

First published 2010

ISBN: 978-1-898565-04-8



The following abbreviations are used:

Grimwade
Arthur Grimwade, *London Goldsmiths 1697–1837: Their Marks and Lives from the Original Registers at Goldsmiths' Hall and Other Sources*, London, rev. edn, 1990

Jones
Kenneth Crisp Jones (ed.), *The Silversmiths of Birmingham and Their Marks 1750–1980*, London, 1981

*Designed by* Chris Jones, Design4Science Ltd
*Printed on 170 gsm Burgo R400 paper by* Conti Tipocolor, Florence, Italy

COVER ILLUSTRATIONS
Front: no. 34
Back: no. 11
Front flap: Centrepiece in the form of a *tempietto*, silver, London, 1800, maker's mark of William Pitts

The roundel motif that adorns this book is taken from a silver-gilt dish of 1787–8, maker's mark of William Pitts, in *The Classical Ideal: English Silver 1760–1840*, cat. no. 45, lent by Timothy Schroder, Esq.

# Foreword

Our loan exhibition of Rundell, Bridge & Rundell silver and other works of art, held in our showrooms five years ago, gave us enormous pleasure and helped bring a deeper understanding and appreciation of a subject we love. Since then our business has grown from strength to strength.

With our latest loan exhibition we are taking a step in a new and wonderful direction. Neo-classical is a term often loosely used. Our hope is that this will be a defining show bringing fuller meaning to a much admired style and new excitement to those who collect it. This selection from our stock, held in conjunction with the exhibition, offers a fresh look at this style that has never gone out of fashion.

Koopman Rare Art is determined to explore the finest silver available on behalf of all our new and existing clients. If there is a rule we follow, it is always to buy the best and most magnificent of any period. We often say we are guided by style and quality and this exhibition is the perfect example of that approach.

It has taken many days, weeks and months and a great deal of research and travel to seek out the treasures offered here. We hope that you appreciate the effort put in by all our staff to present this highly select choice of objects, and that you will enjoy both this selection and the many other beautiful items we have to offer at all times in our gallery.

**Lewis Smith & Timo Koopman**

I

# Pair of two-handled cups and covers on stands

**Marks**: London, 1766 and 1767
**Maker's mark**: John Parker I & Edward Wakelin
Grimwade, no. 1602
**Published**: H. Clifford, *Silver in London: The Parker and Wakelin Partnership, 1760–1776* (London, 2004), fig. 143, p. 110

These noble vases on stands owe much to the distinctive baroque style of the architect and designer William Kent, but they also reflect the new decorative vocabulary of neo-classicism that took the world by storm during the 1760s. This is hardly surprising given that these urns were owned by Assheton Curzon (1733–1820), whose brother Nathaniel Curzon employed Robert Adam to create stunning interiors in the new neo-classical style at Kedleston, his house in Derbyshire.

According to an inscription, one of these cups was given to Assheton Curzon's bride, Dorothy, by his mother, Dame Mary Curzon, on the day of her marriage, 6 February 1766. Dorothy was the sister of Richard, Earl Grosvenor and the wheat-ear decoration on the cup was probably inspired by the Grosvenor family arms which incorporate a wheat sheaf. The cup appears in the business records of Parker & Wakelin, the fashionable retailers, as "a fine Chaisd Cup and Cover and Stand" costing £59 19s, with an additional £16 2s for gilding and 9s for engraving the inscription. The corresponding entry, however, in Parker & Wakelin's suppliers' ledger shows that the actual makers were James Ansill & Stephen Gilbert, former apprentices to Wakelin. Their charge for the cup was only £23, allowing the retailers a mark-up of over 100 per cent. The other cup was given by Mrs Elizabeth Milnes, "40 years Servant to Lady Curzon", to Assheton Curzon.

Height 16 in. (40.6 cm)
Weight 224 oz. (6966 g)

# 2

# Pair of two-light candelabra and pair of candlesticks

Silver
**Marks:** London, 1772, the branches 1773
**Maker's mark:** John Carter II
Grimwade, no. 1214

These candlesticks are formed as Ionic columns, which are characterized by the bold scrolls at each corner of the capital. Their carefully worked-out proportions afford a sense of grace and elegance to a dining table. The Five Orders of Architecture were an essential element of classicism. First codified by the Renaissance architect Sebastiano Serlio in 1540, they were five styles of column, each with a different capital. In the eighteenth century various publications formulated the correct proportions of height, diameter and size of the column, most notably Sir William Chambers's *Treatise on the Decorative Part of Civil Architecture* of 1759.

Height candelabra: 17 ½ in. (44.2 cm)
Width candelabra: 12 ½ in. (32 cm)
Weight 137 oz. 12 dwt. (4280 g)

# 3
# Four wine coasters

Silver, fruitwood, felt
**Marks**: Birmingham, 1773
**Maker's mark**: Matthew Boulton & John Fothergill
Jones, p. 357, col. 2, no. 3
**Heraldry**: Engraved crest of Vere, as borne by Charles Vere, who married Martha Lucas on 4 June 1771

Matthew Boulton's achievement was the subject of a major exhibition in Birmingham in 2009. The son of a Birmingham "toy maker" (a maker of small items such as buttons), he built up a company that produced coins, medals and high-quality wares in Sheffield plate. He also sought to develop the silver manufacturing side of his business and in 1762 established the famous Soho factory just outside Birmingham with John Fothergill, who acted as sales manager. Both Boulton and Fothergill worked hard to establish an assay office in Birmingham, which finally opened in 1773 together with one in Sheffield. This meant that the firm's silver objects did not have to make the long journey to Chester to be assayed and hallmarked.

These wine coasters, part of a service of silver supplied by Boulton & Fothergill for Charles Vere, a country squire, are struck with the earliest Birmingham marks and the date letter "A" for 1773. The Birmingham town mark is an anchor, that of Sheffield a crown, and it is said that these commemorate the many lengthy meetings that took place in the Crown and Anchor inn in Charing Cross, London, between the delegates from Birmingham and Sheffield during their long stints lobbying Parliament. Other items from the Vere service are illustrated in the exhibition catalogue *The Classical Ideal: English Silver, 1760–1840*, nos. 14–15 and 17.

Height 2 in. (5 cm)
Diameter 4 ⅞ in. (12.5 cm)

# 4
# Twelve dinner plates

**Design**: Robert Adam
**Marks**: London, 1773
**Maker's mark**: John Carter II, one a replacement by C.J. Vander
Grimwade, no. 1214
**Heraldry**: Engraved arms of Sir Watkin Williams-Wynn, 4th Bt., of Wynnstay, Wales
**Provenance**: Sir Watkin Williams-Wynn, 4th Bt., by descent to Sir Watkin Williams-Wynn, 8th Bt., sale, Sotheby's, London, 10 October 1946
**Published**: Oliver Fairclough, "Sir Watkin Williams-Wynn and Robert Adam: commissions for silver 1768–80", *The Burlington Magazine*, CXXXVII [1995], pp. 55–9

One of the most celebrated dinner services of the eighteenth century, the Williams-Wynn service was commissioned by a Welsh baronet, Sir Watkin Williams-Wynn, in 1773. Williams-Wynn had been a major client of the Royal Goldsmith Thomas Heming for several years. Among his purchases from Heming was a magnificent neo-classical style punch-bowl, now in the collection of the National Museum of Wales, which is included in the exhibition *The Classical Ideal*. By 1773, Williams-Wynn owed Heming over £2,000 so it is perhaps not surprising that he turned to another supplier of silverware, Joseph Creswell, who had premises in the Adelphi, the Adam brothers' fashionable terrace, for his most significant silver purchase – a complete dinner service. The Adams were designing a town house at 20 St James's Square for Williams-Wynn. Its elegant neo-classical interior included a fashionable "eating room" for which they provided designs for the furniture and door fittings. To complement this, they designed candelabra, soup and sauce tureens, plates and dishes, the drawings for which survive in Sir John Soane's Museum. Other items from the service are illustrated in the exhibition catalogue *The Classical Ideal: English Silver, 1760–1840*, nos. 11. 16, 18 and 21–3. Although dispersed at auction in the 1940s, the Williams-Wynn service remains a fascinating instance of Georgian patronage.

Diameter 9 ½ in. (24.2 cm)
Weight 214 oz. (6680 g)

# 5
# Cream jug and sugar bowl

Silver
**Marks**: London, 1775
**Maker's mark**: John Robins
Grimwade, no. 1623

The attractive alternating vertical bands of matting and polished surfaces on this cream jug and sugar basin are similar to the decoration on the magnificent tea service made for the actor David Garrick and his wife by James Young & Orlando Jackson in 1774, now in the Victoria and Albert Museum. The entwined serpent handles, however, are based on Renaissance design prints.

Height 6 ½ in. (16.2 cm)/4 ¾ in. (12 cm)
Weight 20 oz. 10 dwt. (640 g)

6

# Pair of cassolettes

Silver
**Marks**: London, 1773
**Maker's mark**: Emick Romer
Grimwade, no. 638

The fashion for small vases with pierced covers to burn perfume came from France in the seventeenth century. Renodæus' *Medicinal Dispensatory*, translated by Richard Tomlinson in 1657, directs the reader to "Put [perfume] in a brasen or silver pot which the Vulgar call a cassolet". William Beckford speaks romantically of "Silver braziers and cassolettes diffusing a very pleasant perfume" in his *Italy, with sketches of Spain and Portugal* of 1834. Cassolettes were made in Sèvres porcelain, while in England Matthew Boulton made "essence vases" or "essence pots" in ormolu and Blue John. Examples in silver, however, are extremely rare.

Height 10 ¼ in. (26 cm)
Weight 27 oz. 12 dwt. (860 g)

7

# Four wine coolers

Silver
**Marks**: London, 1776
**Maker's mark**: Daniel Smith & Robert Sharp
Grimwade, no. 506
**Heraldry**: The arms are those of Blatchford of Osborne, Isle of Wight, impaling those of Downham

Height 9 ¾ in. (25 cm)
Weight 213 oz. 10 dwt. (6643 g)

**Provenance**: Maldwin Drummond, Esq., sale, Christie's, London, 10 November 1971
**Published**: Michael Clayton, *Christie's Pictorial History of English and American Silver* (Oxford, 1985), illus. p. 232, no. 2

The wine cooler for a single bottle of wine, as opposed to a wine cistern, enjoyed a brief vogue in the first decades of the eighteenth century but then seems to have fallen out of fashion. The form was revived in the 1770s and this important set of four examples is among the earliest known from this decade.

8

# Pair of meat dishes

Silver
**Marks**: Birmingham, 1777
**Maker's mark**: Matthew Boulton & John Fothergill
Jones, p. 357, col. 2, no. 3

Surviving work from the partnership of Matthew Boulton and John Fothergill is rare, and pairs of meat dishes virtually unique. The tied reeded borders on these dishes are identical to those on Boulton & Fothergill's service for Mrs Elizabeth Monatagu, the celebrated intellectual of the period, who was known as "the Queen of the Bluestockings".

Width 16 ¾ in. (42.5 cm)
Weight 62 oz. (1928 g)

# 9

# Centrepiece on stand

Silver
**Marks**: London, 1777
**Maker's mark**: John Wakelin & William Tayler
Grimwade, no. 1764
**Provenance**: Bulgari, Rome; anonymous sale, Christie's. Rome, 9–10 December 1999, lot 307

Width 15 ¾ in. (40 cm)
Weight 81 oz. (2520 g)

# 10

# Punch-bowl

Silver
**Marks**: London, 1777
**Maker's mark**: John Wakelin & William Tayler
Grimwade, no. 1764

Height 8⅞ in. (22.5 cm)
Weight 80 oz. (2500 g)

11

# Pair of sauce tureens and covers

Silver
**Marks**: London, 1777
**Maker's mark**: Andrew Fogelberg
Grimwade, no. 32

Width 7 in. (18 cm)
Weight 43 oz. (1337 g)

12

# Pair of sauce tureens

Silver
**Marks**: London, 1777
**Maker's mark**: Robert Hennell
Grimwade, no. 2311

These elegant sauce tureens are identical to the twelve examples which form part of the Holkham Service, made for Thomas William Coke (1754–1843) in 1776–7. The Hennell workshop was commissioned to produce the sauce tureens and salts from that service, and these tureens show that they continued to produce this extremely successful design for other clients (see the exhibition catalogue, *The Classical Ideal*, p. 43).

Width 8 in. (20.4 cm)
Weight 47 oz. 10 dwt. (1480 g)

13

# Cake basket

Silver
**Marks**: London, 1777
**Maker's mark**: William Plummer
Grimwade, no. 3255

Of exceptionally large size, this basket is characterized by the superb quality of its piercing, done by hand with a tiny fret saw. By the late 1770s much of this type of piercing was done by a steam press. Machined piercing is evident by its regularity but close examination of the sides of this basket show minute saw marks and irregularities that reveal handwork.

Width 15 ½ in. (39.2 cm)
Weight 51 oz. 8 dwt. (1600 g)

# 14
# Pair of candlesticks

Silver
**Marks**: Birmingham, 1780
**Maker's mark**: Matthew Boulton & John Fothergill
Jones, p. 357, col. 2, no. 3

This model of candlestick was designed for the partnership of Boulton & Fothergill by the architect James Wyatt (1746–1813). Wyatt came from a dynasty of Midlands builders and masons which had strong links with the Soho Manufactory (a Wyatt was one of Boulton's foremen). James Wyatt created elegant neo-classical designs which were often much lighter in feeling than the work of Robert Adam but professionally he was notoriously unreliable. He died in a carriage accident in 1813.

Height 13 in. (33 cm)

# 15
# Four salts

Silver-gilt
**Marks**: London, 1783
**Maker's mark**: William Pitts
Grimwade, no. 3263

**Provenance**: John, 3rd Duke of Dorset (1745–1799), then by descent to his son, George, 4th Duke of Dorset (1793–1815), then by descent to his first cousin, Charles, 2nd Viscount Sackville and 5th Duke of Dorset (1767–1843), then by descent to the second daughter of George, 4th Duke of Dorset, Lady Elizabeth Sackville-West (d. 1870), later Baroness Buckhurst, wife of George, 5th Earl De La Warre (1791–1869), who assumed her paternal name and arms by Royal Licence in addition to those of West in 1843, then by descent to their fourth son, Mortimer, 1st Baron Sackville

Burke's Economical Reform Act of 1782 closed down the Jewel House, the department of the Royal Household that had issued silver for royal officials such as ambassadors, and the Royal Goldsmith Thomas Heming was dismissed. His rivals Jefferys & Jones of Cockspur Street successfully tendered for the much-reduced business of providing silver for the Crown. These salts were part of a dinner service supplied by them for John, 3rd Duke of Dorset's embassy to Paris in 1784. Their account, dated 1 April 1784, now in the Kent Archives Office, Maidstone, lists "12 salts 92 [oz.] 8 [dwt.] fa[shioning] 50/. [s] each, £55.8.4".

Width 5 ¾ in. (14.5 cm)
Weight 30 oz. (951 g)

# 16

# Tea caddy on stand

Silver-gilt
**Marks**: London, 1785
**Maker's mark**: Andrew Fogelberg & Stephen Gilbert
**Heraldry**: Engraved crest of a martlet

The goldsmith Andrew Fogelberg, also identified as Anders Fogelberg, was born in Sweden in 1732 and apprenticed to a goldsmith in Halmsted in 1746. He is thought to have come to England from his homeland around 1770; he is recorded as a plateworker in Church Street, Soho, in 1773. By 1780 he was in partnership with Stephen Gilbert, who had been apprenticed to Edward Wakelin in 1752. From their address at 29 Church Street, St Anne's, Soho, the output of this partnership was of exceptional quality and of a restrained classical nature, often highlighted by the use of small cameo medallions. The ingenious use of a stand on square tapering legs applied with swags, from which one can lift the caddy, is reminiscent of the decorative sketches of Sir William Chambers (1723–1796), architect to King George III, but perhaps closest in feel is a pencil sketch by Chambers's rival James Wyatt (1746–1813) in an album of drawings acquired by the Vicomte de Noailles in 1946. A matching teapot on stand is in the exhibition catalogue *The Classical Ideal: English Silver, 1760–1840*, no. 42.

Width 6 ½ in. (16.5 cm)
Weight 22 oz. 15 dwt. (685 g)

# 17
# Pair of *verrières*

Silver-gilt
**Marks**: London, 1786
**Maker's mark**: Daniel Smith & Robert Sharp
Grimwade, no. 506

Width 15 ¼ in. (38.5 cm)
Weight 182 oz. 12 dwt. (5680 g)

While the monteith, a bowl with scalloped rim from which wine glasses could be cooled in iced water, enjoyed a vogue in England from the 1680s onwards, its use had all but died out by the 1720s. The Continental version, elliptical rather than circular, lived on, however, and large quantities were made at the Sèvres porcelain manufactory from the 1760s onwards. British and Irish fascination with French customs and fashions, especially after the Treaty of Paris in 1763, saw the adoption of a number of French forms including the *verrière*.

These magnificent silver-gilt examples were made for John Fitzgibbon, later 1st Earl of Clare (c. 1749–1802), who was Attorney-General for Ireland in 1783 and appointed Lord Chancellor of Ireland in 1789. He persuaded George III to oppose the lifting of the restrictions that had been placed on practising Catholics since the sixteenth century and was instrumental in the downfall of the Prime Minister William Pitt.

# 18

# Pair of royal four-light candelabra

Silver-gilt
**Marks**: Paris, 1789
**Maker's mark**: Henry Auguste
**Signature**: "Auguste Fils Orfèvre du Roi Paris 1789"
**Inscription**: "Duke of York's Plate"
**Heraldry**: Engraved arms of Archibald Kennedy. 12th Earl of Cassilis and later 1st Marquess of Ailsa
**Provenance**: Frederick Augustus, Duke of York and Albany KG (1763–1827), second son of George III, sale, Christie's, London, 20 March 1827, lots 89, 90, 91 or 92, purchased by Thomas Brothers; Archibald Kennedy, 12th Earl of Cassilis and 1st Marquess of Ailsa (1770–1846) of Culzean Castle, Ayrshire, then by descent

French neo-classical silver, which was fashionable in late Georgian Britain, was quite different from that produced by London designers and silversmiths. The contrast between areas of smooth polished silver or silver-gilt and finely chased applied decoration was exploited to the full, perhaps no more successfully than in the work of Henry Auguste. The son of the great Royal goldsmith Robert-Joseph Auguste, Henry enjoyed great success in the 1780s. His association with the neo-classical designer Jean-Guillaume Moitte (1746–1810), who had returned from Italy in 1773, produced candlesticks, ewers and basins, usually of silver-gilt, of unrivalled elegance. Auguste, however, was unlucky in seeing his business all but collapse with the Revolution.

Nevertheless, British clients such as the aesthete and collector William Beckford continued to visit him in Paris until the advent of the Terror and subsequent war made travel impossible. Although he admired Auguste's refined version of neo-classicism (Beckford's 1822 sale catalogue of Fonthill Abbey, no doubt much of it written by Beckford himself, described Auguste's work as "worthy of the best period of Grecian art" and "finished with unrivalled excellence"), Beckford, with characteristic waspishness, referred to Auguste as the "slippery Eel". Beckford purchased a number of pieces from Auguste including a gold ewer. A silver-gilt ewer and basin, one of two sets he acquired, can now be seen, along with Moitte's drawing, in the new Gilbert Gallery in the Victoria and Albert Museum.

It is known that Auguste also exported silver to Britain, possibly working in conjunction with Paul Storr (see no. 22), and by the time of Napoleon and the establishment of the Empire, his Paris business was thriving once again. Auguste was at the forefront of the new fashion for highly finished silver-gilt that sought to create an aura of gold around the emperor. He supplied part of the "Grand Vermeil", the magnificent service presented to the Emperor and Empress by the City of Paris following their coronation in 1804. Auguste's success was to be short-lived, however, for in 1809 he was again in financial difficulties. Later that year he was apprehended at Calais attempting to ship

**Jean-Guillaume Moitte (1746–1810),** ***Design for a candelabrum*****, pen and wash.**

twenty-two crates of silver and gemstones to England to escape his creditors. He died a pauper in Port-au-Prince in 1816.

It is ironic that Frederick Augustus, Duke of York, the second son of George III and Queen Charlotte, who was to be Commander-in-Chief of the army during Britain's war with the young French Republic, should have purchased the finest Paris silver. These candelabra form part of a set of twelve that belonged to the duke. On the duke's death in 1827 his executors took the unprecedented step of placing his collections up for public auction. "The sacrifice was indeed great," observed the auctioneer James Christie the younger as lot after lot sold for a pittance. The candelabra, sold individually, realized between £36 and £42 each and were ultimately separated, as pairs, to different owners. A pair is now in the Metropolitan Museum of Art in New York, and another is in the Palace of the Legion of Honor in San Francisco.

The present pair was acquired by Archibald Kennedy, 12th Earl of Cassilis, whose seat, Culzean Castle on the west coast of Scotland, had been transformed from a wind-swept ruin into a magnificent pile in the "Castle style" by Robert Adam. Kennedy's second son married one of the daughters of the Duke of Clarence and his mistress the actress Mrs Jordan. When the duke became King William IV in 1830, Kennedy was created Marquess of Ailsa. The candelabra remained in the family until last year.

Height 23 ½ in. (60 cm)
Weight 295 oz. (9180 g)

## 19

# Soup tureen and cover

Silver
**Marks**: London, 1793
**Maker's mark**: Robert Sharp
Grimwade, no. 2436

Width 19 in. (48 cm)
Weight 101 oz. 10 dwt. (3160 g)

20

# Cup and cover

Silver-gilt
**Marks**: London, 1793
**Maker's mark**: William Holmes
Grimwade, no. 3161
**Signature**: "Pickett & Rundell fecit Londini"
**Inscription**: "DONCASTER CUP / 1793 / Richard Beaumont Esq. / Christopher Wilson Esq. / Stewards"

Won by Oberon in 1793, the Doncaster Cup, still among the most celebrated flat races run for annually, was established in 1766. In the eighteenth century it was run over a four-mile course, and was a noted contest for horses that were "stayers".

William Holmes was one of the most assured proponents of the neo-classical style. He appears to have been working as early as 1762, although, as a member of the Lorimers' Company, he was not admitted a freeman of the Goldsmiths' Company. He was in partnership with David Whyte from 1764 to 1767, and with Nicholas Dumée from 1773 to 1776. He specialized in large-scale work with highly finished cast components such as this cup and cover. He was the maker of the magnificent pair of ewers commissioned by Thomas William Coke (1754–1842) of Holkham Hall in Norfolk, which is illustrated in the catalogue of the concurrent exhibition *The Classical Ideal: English Silver, 1760–1840*, no. 31 and on its cover.

Height 23 in. (58.5 cm)
Weight 202 oz. 10 dwt. (6300 g)

Doncaster Cup
Richard Beaumont Esq.
Christopher Wilson Esq.
Stewards

## 21

# Pair of three-light candelabra

Silver
**Marks**: London, 1795
**Maker's mark**: John Scofield
Grimwade, no. 1670
**Heraldry**: Engraved arms of Tatton of Kenworthy and Withenshaw, Cheshire

Height 16 ⅝ in. (32 cm)
Weight 123 oz. (3840 g)

## 22

# Set of four sauce tureens

**Marks**: Britannia standard, London, 1797
**Maker's mark**: Paul Storr
Grimwade, no. 2234

Height 4 ½ in. (11.4 cm)
Width 7 in. (18 cm)
Diameter 4 ¾ in. (12 cm)
Weight 89 oz. 8 dwt. (2700 g)

These sauce tureens are part of an interesting group of silver struck with Britannia standard marks and dating from 1797 and 1798. The group comprises candlesticks, candelabra, wine coolers and tureens, all with highly finished applied borders, in the French neo-classical style. Most bear the mark of Paul Storr, although at Corpus Christi College, Cambridge, there is a pair of candelabra, one by Paul Storr of 1798 and the other of 1797, with the maker's mark FM in script in a rectangle. The candelabra are based on designs by the neo-classical designer Jean-Guillaume Moitte (1746–1810), who is known to have worked for Henry Auguste, the great Paris goldsmith (see no. 18). It is likely that these pieces were either imported into England from France as finished articles, or as component parts, and hallmarked before sale in London. The presence of Britannia standard marks is explained by the fact that the French 1st *titre* silver standard is higher than the English Britannia standard of 958 parts per 1,000. Auguste is known to have travelled regularly to England and to have had many English clients.

# 23
# Inkstand

Silver
**Marks**: London, 1805
**Maker's mark**: John Edwards III
Grimwade, no. 1273
**Inscription**: "Truth"
**Provenance**: The Executors of the late Herbert Rothbarth, Esq., sale, Christie's, London, 25 May 1960, lot 42

Width 5 in. (12.5 cm)
Weight 16 oz. 14 dwt. (520 g)

## 24
# Five meat dishes

Silver
**Marks**: London, 1823
**Maker's mark**: Philip Rundell for Rundell, Bridge & Rundell
Grimwade, no. 2228

**Provenance**: William Beckford (1760–1844), by descent to his second daughter Susan Euphemia, who married Alexander, 10th Duke of Hamilton (1767–1852), then by descent to William, 12th Duke of Hamilton (1845–1895), sale, Christie's, London, 25 February 1948, lots 139–142

William Beckford, aesthete and collector, was a prodigious buyer of plate throughout his life. These dishes were purchased shortly after he had sold Fonthill Abbey to the Scottish gunpowder millionaire John Farquhar and moved to Bath. But the urge to build overtook him once again and he began work on his celebrated tower.

Width two: 17 in. (43 cm); two: 15 1/8 in. (38.5 cm); one: 14 in. (36 cm)
Weight 263 oz. (8180 g)

# 25
# Pair of wine coolers on stands

Silver
**Marks**: London, 1807
**Maker's mark**: Benjamin Smith II
**Heraldry**: Applied arms of the 4th Duke of Richmond and Lennox (1764–1819)
**Provenance**: By descent to the 9th Duke of Richmond and Gordon, sale, Sotheby's, London, 4 July 1946, lot 163 (a set of eight)

The same model of wine cooler raised on stands supported by imperial lions was favoured by members of the royal family. A set of six applied with the arms of one of the sons of George III was sold from the collection of the Duke of Cambridge at Christie's in 1904. A pair from this set was sold from the collection of Ferdinand and Imelda Marcos at Christie's, 10 January 1991, lot 51.

Of the 4th Duke of Richmond, the diarist Croker quipped that he appears to have been born, as he was to die, in a barn: "his mother Lady Louisa was taken ill when on a fishing party, and there was only time to carry her to a neighbouring farmyard". At an early age the duke achieved notoriety by his duel with the Duke of York, second son of George III, on Wimbledon Common on 26 May 1789 (see no. 18). In 1806 he succeeded to the dukedom and the following year he was appointed Lord Lieutenant of Ireland. These wine coolers form part of the prodigious service of plate that accompanied him to Dublin. The duke kept up such a regal state in Dublin that on his return to England he could not afford to live at Goodwood, his seat in Sussex, but was forced to take up residence in Brussels. It was there, in a coach-maker's depot in the rue de la Blanchisserie, that his duchess gave the famous ball on the night before the Battle of Waterloo.

In 1818 the duke was appointed Governor-General of Canada, where his extreme views led to a clash not only with the French-Canadian party but also with the indigenous population. His term of office was cut short the following year by his death from a bite from a rabid fox, given to him, it was said, by a local Indian tribe.

Height 12 in. (30 cm)
Weight 338 oz. (10512 g)

## 26

# Salver

Silver-gilt
**Marks**: London, 1808
**Maker's mark**: Benjamin Smith II
Grimwade, no. 229

Diam. 12 in. (30.5 cm)
Weight 61 oz. (1840 g)

# 27
# Pair of dressing-table candlesticks

Silver
**Marks**: Birmingham, 1809
**Maker's mark**: Matthew Boulton & Co.
Jones, p. 357, col. 1, no. 5

Height 7 ¾ in. (19.7 cm)

## 28

# Royal egg stand

Silver-gilt
**Marks**: London, 1809
**Maker's mark**: Rebeccah Emes & Edward Barnard I, the spoons Eley, Fearn & Chawner
Grimwade, nos. 2309 and 3114
**Inscription**: "HIS ROYAL HIGHNESS, THE DUKE OF CAMBRIDGE K.G. FROM THE SALE JUNE 1904 COMMANDER IN CHIEF 1856-1895"

**Provenance**: Adolphus Frederick, 1st Duke of Cambridge (1774–1850), seventh son of King George III, by descent to his son, the 2nd duke, His Royal Highness The Duke of Cambridge KG, KT, KP (1819–1904), sale, Christie's, London, June 6–7, 1904, lot 242 (to Spink)

Like his brothers the Dukes of York and Sussex, Adolphus, 1st Duke of Cambridge (1774-1850), was a prodigious collector of silver and silver-gilt. His son, George, 2nd Duke of Cambridge (1818-1904), served for many years as the Commander-in-Chief of the Army.

Width 7 ¾ in. (19.7 cm)
Weight 40 oz. 10 dwt. (1259 g)

# 29
# Four wine coolers

Silver
**Marks**: London, 1809 and 1811
**Maker's mark**: Paul Storr for Rundell, Bridge & Rundell
Grimwade, no. 2234
Heraldry: Engraved arms of Howard, for Bernard Edward, 12th Duke of Norfolk (1765–1842)

These imposing wine coolers are typical of the silver in the confident imperial style produced by Rundell, Bridge & Rundell during the Regency period. With the great Paul Storr at the helm of their Soho silver workshops, the firm produced work of the highest quality. The Dukes of Norfolk were among Rundell's biggest patrons, the 11th and 12th Dukes spending over £12,000 with the firm between 1811 and 1820. These coolers, described in Rundell's bills as "handsome shell Ice Pails with Lion's head handles", cost nearly £100 each, with an additional 3 guineas for engraving armorials on each one (see Christopher Hartop, *Royal Goldsmiths: the Art of Rundell & Bridge 1797–1843*, exh. cat., 2005, p. 68, fig. 58).

Height 9 ¼ in. (23.5 cm)
Weight 479 oz. (14900 g)

SOLA VIRTUS INVICTA

## 30

# Twenty-four dinner plates and twelve soup plates

Diameter dinner plates 10 ½ in. (26 cm);
soup plates 10 ½ in. (26.7 cm)
Weight 829 oz. (25784 g)

Silver
**Marks**: London, 1810
**Maker's mark**: Paul Storr for Rundell, Bridge & Rundell
Grimwade, no. 2234
**Heraldry**: Engraved arms of Balfour impaling those of Maitland, as borne by James Balfour (d. 1845) of Bailbirnie, Fife, who married Eleanor Maitland (1790–1869), daughter of James, 8th Earl of Lauderdale
**Provenance**: Christie's, London, 16 July 1930
**Published**: N.M. Penzer, *Paul Storr 1771–1844, Silversmith and Goldsmith* (London, 1954), p. 254

# 31
# Centrepiece

Silver
**Marks**: London, 1814
**Maker's mark**: Paul Storr for Rundell, Bridge & Rundell
Grimwade, no. 2234

Height 19 ¾ in. (50 cm)
Weight 241 oz. (7500 g)

# 32
# Soup tureen, cover and stand

Silver
**Marks**: London, 1815
**Maker's mark**: Paul Storr for Rundell, Bridge & Rundell
Grimwade, no. 2234
**Heraldry**: Engraved arms of Menteath of Kerse, Stirlingshire, quarterly with those of Stirling

Width 21 in. (54 cm)
Weight 261 oz. (8120 g)

## 33

# Pair of Warwick Vases

Silver
**Marks**: London, 1819
**Maker's mark**: Paul Storr for Rundell, Bridge & Rundell
Grimwade, no. 2234
**Signature**: "Green Ward et Green Londini Fecerunt"

Height 9 ¾ in. (24.8 cm)
Weight 396 oz. (12340 g)

Found in fragments at the bottom of a lake at Hadrian's Villa near Rome in 1770, the Warwick Vase is a colossal marble vase measuring nearly six feet high. Acquired by Sir William Hamilton, English envoy to Naples, it was sold to his nephew the Earl of Warwick who set it up in the courtyard at Warwick Castle. The vase was not without its critics.The Hon. John Byng, later Viscount Torrington, author of a series of fascinating and at times irascible journals of his rides through England, described it on a visit to Warwick Castle as "a vulgar overgrown Roman basin".

Piranesi did an engraving of the vase in 1778 and these prints inspired versions in silver, in the form of wine coolers and even salts, produced by the Royal Goldsmiths, Rundell, Bridge & Rundell. In 1812 they supplied a set of eight silver-gilt examples to the Prince Regent; a set of four made for his brother, the Duke of York, was included in the sale of the duke's silver in 1827. Shortly after this the firm began producing cast reductions of the vase itself and the following year Sir Edward Thomason recorded that there had been "much talk that the Earl of Warwick had at last permitted a model of the splendid vase, at Warwick Castle, to be modelled on the spot, provided Lord Lonsdale would have it made in silver". Sadly, however, Lord Lonsdale's version in silver was never made; Rundell's went as far as having William Theed, one of their modellers, make a life-size wax model but their estimate, of £30,000 – "£5,000 more or less" – was not approved by Lonsdale and the scheme was abandoned. Rundell's did succeed in making several life-size bronze models of the vase, one of which sits outside the Senate House in Cambridge (C. Hartop, *Royal Goldsmiths: the Art of Rundell & Bridge 1797–1843*, 2005, pp. 117–18).

# 34
# Presentation vase and stand

Silver-gilt
**Marks**: London, 1822
**Maker's mark**: Philip Rundell for Rundell,
Bridge & Rundell
Grimwade, no. 2228
**Signature**: "RUNDELL BRIDGE ET RUNDELL AURIFICES REGIS LONDINI"
**Inscription**: "A TRIBUTE OF GRATEFUL REMEMBRANCE FROM THE OFFICERS OF THE HYDERABAD DIVISION OF H.H. THE NIZAM'S REGULAR TROOPS TO HENRY RUSSELL ESQUIRE"
**Provenance**: Sir Henry Russell (1783–1852), 2nd Bt., then by descent
**Published**: Constance, Lady Russell, *Swallowfield and Its Owners*, London, 1901, p. 256

The ancient vases illustrated by Piranesi in his book *Vasi* of 1778 were frequently the inspiration for presentation pieces supplied by the Royal Goldsmiths, Rundell, Bridge & Rundell. This magnificent vase illustrates the collaborative process, of design, modelling and making, that was typical at that time.

Sir Henry Russell was a friend of Sir Francis Chantrey and asked the eminent sculptor to advise on the design of a vase to be presented to him by his fellow officers in India. Chantrey, who undertook work for Rundell's, suggested using the Buckingham Vase, a Roman marble vase belonging to the Earl of Buckingham which had been included by Piranesi in his *Vasi*, as the model. To design the scenes on each side of the vase, Chantrey recommended Thomas Stothard RA, an artist who also did work for Rundell's. The whole was drawn by Burney, a well-known artist of the day, while the elephants' heads and serpents were modelled by Edward Hodges Baily, who was in charge of Rundell's design studio. Rundell's total bill for the vase and stand was £1,100.

**The Buckingham Vase, Giovanni Battista Piranesi, etching from *Vasi, candelabri ... ed antichi*, Rome, 1778.**

Height 28 ⅛ in. (71.5 cm)
Width 14 ½ in. (37 cm)
Weight 546 oz. (17000 g)

FROM THE OFFICERS
HENRY RUSSELL ESQUIRE

# 35
# Centrepiece

Silver
**Marks**: London, 1824
**Maker's mark**: John Bridge for Rundell, Bridge & Rundell
Grimwade, no. 1172
Provenance: Sotheby's, New York, 14 April 1999, lot 213

Inspired by the naturalism of the famous Marine Service made for Frederick, Prince of Wales, in the 1740s, this sumptuous centrepiece is one of the earliest of a small group of versions of this model produced by Rundell, Bridge & Rundell in the 1820s. The firm supplied four of them to King George IV between 1826 and 1829. The design is probably by John Flaxman, who had become chief designer at Rundell's following the death of William Theed in 1817.

Height 15 in. (38 cm)
Weight 343 oz. (10668 g)

# 36
# Four-piece tea and coffee service

Silver-gilt, ivory
**Marks**: London, 1828
**Maker's mark**: John Bridge for Rundell, Bridge & Rundell
Grimwade, no. 1172
**Provenance**: Thomas Hope (1769–1831), by descent,
the Hope Heirlooms, sale, Chrisite's, London, 17 July 1917, lot 4
**Published**: M. Clayton, *The Collectors' Dictionary of the Silver and Gold of Great Britian and Northern Ireland*, 1985, p. 424; V. Brett, *The Sotheby's Directory of Silver*, 1985, no. 1165; C. Hartop, *Royal Goldsmiths: the Art of Rundell & Bridge, 1797–1843* (Cambridge, 2005), p. 133, fig. 130
**Exhibited**: *The Glory of the Goldsmith*, 1989, cat. no. 157; *Royal Goldsmiths: The Art of Rundell & Bridge, 1797–1843,* Koopman Rare Art, 2005, cat. no. 59

The collector and aesthete Thomas Hope (1769–1831) was a regular customer of the Royal Goldsmiths, Rundell, Bridge & Rundell, often ordering silver to his own designs. He had bought a pair of vases with scenes of the Age of Silver and the Age of Gold, identical to one purchased by King George IV in 1827 and in the following year he purchased this tea service in the same style. John Flaxman's elegant Grecian *skyphos* has been adapted by the addition of handles and spouts and applied with panels extolling Britain's naval might.

Height (coffee pot) 12 in. (30.5 cm)
Weight gross: 120 oz. (3751 g)

# 37
# Pair of Gaeta Vases

Bronze, porphyry
Late 18th/early 19th century
**Signature**: "G.ZOFFOLI.F"

Giacomo Zoffoli (c. 1731–1785) and his putative brother Giovanni (c. 1745–1805) were celebrated in Rome as creators of superb bronze reductions of classical sculpture. A visit to their workshop was a must for eighteenth-century travellers doing the Grand Tour. These elegant vases are based on the famous Gaeta Vase by the Athenian sculptor Salpion, which until 1805 served as the baptismal font in Gaeta Cathedral and is now part of the collection of antiquities at the Museo Nazionale in Naples.

The vase is listed in a sales catalogue produced by Giovanni Zoffoli in 1795, priced at 25 *zecchini*, the same price that he charged for a copy of the Medici Vase. The catalogue was sent from Rome by Charles Heathcote Tatham to his fellow architect Henry Holland in London and shortly afterwards Tatham produced a drawing of a *garniture de cheminée* with one of Zoffoli's Gaeta Vases as the centrepiece. Another figures in a similar grouping illustrated as plate XLVIII in Thomas Hope's *Household Furniture and Interior Decoration* published in 1807.

Height 13 ½ in. (33.6 cm)

# NEO-CLASSICAL METALWORK

## Symposium

### Saturday, 19 June 2010, 11 a.m. to 5 p.m.

**11 a.m. Registration and coffee**
Viewing of the exhibition *The Classical Ideal: English Silver, 1760–1840* and study session with neo-classical silver with the curator, Christopher Hartop, at Koopman Rare Art, 53–64 Chancery Lane, London WC2A 1QS

**1 p.m. Buffet lunch and lectures**
at the Royal College of Surgeons of England, 35–43 Lincoln's Inn Fields, London WC2A 3PE

**2 p.m. Welcome and introduction**
Philippa Glanville
Former Keeper of Metalwork, Victoria and Albert Museum, London

**2.10 p.m. Robert Adam: promotion by design**
Dr Steven Parissien
Director, Compton Verney Museum and Gallery, Warwickshire and Visiting Fellow, Kellogg College, University of Oxford

**2:50 p.m. Sir Watkin Williams-Wynn's great dinner service: a group of Adam designs of 1772–3**
Oliver Fairclough, Keeper of Art, National Museum of Wales

**3:30 p.m. Tea**

**4:00 p.m. Boxes formed as bath tubs, and other fashion accessories: neo-classical gold boxes**
Charles Truman
Independent dealer, writer and consultant

**4:40 p.m. Concluding remarks**
Dr Heike Zech
Curator of the Gilbert Collection,
Victoria and Albert Museum

**5:00 p.m. End of programme**

**Three-light candelabrum, silver, London, 1774, maker's mark probably that of John Carter II, part of the dinner service designed by Robert Adam for Sir Watkin Williams-Wynn, 4th Bt.** *Lent by Lloyd's Corporation*

£50 including buffet lunch and tea

To register, or for more information, telephone Carole Weaver on 020 7242 7624 or by e-mail: carole@koopmanrareart.com